My Detour
on Life's Highway

The Story of a Stem Cell Transplant Survivor

Published by Glacier Publishing
40 Oak Street
Southington, CT 06489
(860) 621-7644

Manufactured in the United States of America

My Detour on Life's Highway
The Story of a Stem Cell Transplant Survivor
By Rosemary Champagne

ISBN 0-9650315-7-8
1. Cancer Treatment Therapy
2. Self-Help
3. Spiritual

Printed and Bound in the United States of America

Other Books Available Through Glacier Publishing
Same Game, Different Name (0-9-650315-1-9)
Whalers Trivia Compendium (0-9-650315-0-0)
Forever Whalers (0-9-65315-3-5)
All-Star Dads (0-9650315-4-3)

Glacier Publishing Books are available directly
through the publisher, at bookstores everywhere or
via the internet at amazon.com or barnesnoble.com

Dedication

To my husband Jim,

My daughter Tracey,

My son-in-law Tom,

And my grandson

JAKE.

I will love you forever.

My Detour on Life's Highway

The Story of a Stem Cell Transplant Survivor

Chapters

Acknowledgments

I want to thank God who gave me wisdom to hope.

My parents Tony and Marge who gave me life, love and peace.

My mother-in-law Ida who is my second mom.

My husband Jim who gave me his unconditional love and alwa was there during my darkest days.

My daughter Tracey, my reason to live, who gave me her lo time, and courage to keep going. Her husband Tom for all his lo and support. Both brought into my life a special gift, my grandsc Jake, a gift from God.

My sister Susan and my brother Bob for all their support, lo and wisdom.

My sister Patty who first taught me how to deal with adversity we struggled through my illness. Patty sat by me day and nigh listened to my deepest thoughts. I thank her for her insightf comments and her extraordinary patience.

My brothers-in-law, sisters-in-law, and my nieces and nephe who light up my life.

My special best friend Monica for the time we share together. love you.

My cousin Barbara who helped in the production of this book.

My loyal staff: Terri, Alison, Stacy, Mary, and Joan for their lo support, courage, humor, and for putting up with me, especially f keeping my dream going.

Pam, Paul, and Gil, special friends, who called me daily.

My cancer friends whom I met throughout the years, especial Joyce, and Ginger.

My cousin Joanne and friend Dolores, both nurses, who too time out of their busy day to answer my questions.

Kudos to Ellie Giannelli for her kindness and creative talents the design of the book cover.

A special tip of the hat to Violet and Bill Sierchio.

Special thanks to Janice and Jack Lautier of Glacier Publishir who believed my story could be best told in a book.

Special Thanks

To the following physicians and specialists who played an important role in my life:

Dr. **Anthony Ciardella** of Southington

As my family physician and friend he has become the middleman in my life. I often called him when I just didn't know what to do. I am very comfortable with him. As one of my hairdressing clients he became personally involved in my medical condition. He continues to help me with my mother who has Alzheimer's Disease. He also counseled me when my dad died.

Dr. Ciardella has been with me from day one on this journey. He always finds time to return my phone calls, and he manages to calm my fears. He gives me second opinions on my medical reports and explains medical terms I don't understand. He always makes me feel important in this process.

Dr. **Joseph Bowen**, Hematologist-Oncologist of Waterbury

I met Dr. Bowen five years after I was diagnosed with cancer. I tend to make quick judgments about people. With Dr. Bowen, I was correct. He never made me feel uncomfortable. When we discussed lymphoma, I always cried. I was embarrassed, but he told me I wouldn't be normal if I didn't cry.

Dr. Bowen has been very helpful during my chemotherapy. He has monitored my lymphoma carefully for over nine years. He suggested a stem cell transplant when my lymphoma changed to a more aggressive stage. I am forever grateful.

Dr. **Dennis Cooper**, Oncologist of New Haven, Clinical Director of the stem cell transplant program at Yale New Haven Hospital

Dr. Cooper greets you with a calm approach and an intelligent attitude. Any questions I had he gave me the answers in language I could understand. He explained the stem transplant extremely well. One day when he noticed I was upset in my hospital room he found time in his busy schedule to sit down and talk to me. He helped change my mood.

Dr. Cooper is personal enough to let you know that he loves the Chicago Cubs. He is also private enough to never show his own emotions. I thank him as well as Dr. Stewart Seropian, Dr Michael DiGiouanna, Betsey D'Andrea RN, Dana Belliveau RN, all the nurses in the Clinic and on the eighth floor Oncology Unit at the Yale New Haven Children's Hospital, for their help, love and support.

Dr. Cooper . . . I will carry a special place for you in my prayers and my heart.

Preface

We travel many roads in a lifetime. We quickly learn it is the detours that are the most challenging. This book is about overcoming a detour.

Chemotherapy, Radiology, Hospitals, and Doctors were not part of my travel plans. I was 39 years old at the time of my diagnosis of Non-Hodgkin's Lymphoma.

I had never heard of stem cell transplant until I was told that it might be a solution to make me healthy again.

I am living proof that this medical procedure works.

Introduction

I decided to write this book four months after my stem cell transplant because I was tired of explaining to people just exactly what it was. Many people have heard of a bone marrow transplant. A stem cell transplant is similar.

Since I had Non-Hodgkin's Lymphoma, I was a good candidate for this stem cell procedure. It had been a trying time, both emotionally and physically, because I did not know what to expect. I sought to research articles about this type of transplant but I found limited information. Maybe the best source of information was a small booklet at the hospital where I underwent the procedure. After reading the information I found it gratifying for cancer patients to learn about the progress of cancer treatment.

Yale New Haven Hospital is a medical teaching hospital where the staff and interns are dedicated professionals. I recommend patients and their families learn all they can about cancer treatment and what a loved one must undergo. It helped my husband, daughter, and my son-in-law to carry me through my biggest challenge.

I have survived cancer for 14 years. You can survive. It is my hope to reach people and their families through my ordeal. That's why I decided to put my story in a book.

The first step in the journey is to believe in yourself. That was something my parents taught me at a young age.

The next step is religion, especially prayer and meditation.

God does have a plan for all of us. We must keep looking for it.

I don't have to remind anyone about anxiety connected with

every day living. Cancer carries much, much more. It is about acceptance, chemotherapy, and radiation. It is about overcoming fears of the unknown. It is about living as much as it is about dying. It is also about surviving.

We should never question our quality of life, the need for others or the impact of religion. Reading books, praying every day, talking to family and friends and asking questions helped me overcome my illness. There were days when my state of mind was very traumatic for my spouse. There were also very lonely days.

When you are sick, you can sense that relatives and friends feel helpless as well. You will feel rejection when an insurance carrier denies a claim. You will feel ignored when close friends do not visit.

You will, however, realize the enormous strength of your family and what its love can do. You will gain greater faith in God. You will find the courage to conquer this severe illness.

I met plenty of people on my detour. I guess we are universal friends, eternally linked because we survived cancer. Like others, stem cell transplant enabled me to find "new" life.

Chapter 1

MY FAMILY

Teach a child to choose the right path,
and when he is older he will remain upon it.

Proverbs 22:6

My name is Rosemary Tarantino Champagne. My friends consider me a happy-go-lucky person who has always loved life. I grew up in a close knit family, the youngest of four children. My home is Southington, a central Connecticut community in Hartford County best known for its many apple orchards.

My parents were never afraid to show their love to my two sisters, my brother, or me. We were taught to be honest and respect others. The family was the center of our lives. Mom stayed home to care for us. There was always the aroma of homemade sauce throughout the house. Mom loved to cook especially pasta. She only went to work when my brother started college. Like my father, she found employment in a local factory. My dad, who enjoyed planting a garden, playing golf, and a good glass of wine, was a toolmaker at a local firm.

I married my high school sweetheart on September 4, 1967. It was two days before my 22nd birthday. Jim Champagne also grew up in a large family. He was the second of six children. What attracted me to Jim was his smile, his patience, his understanding. I marveled at how he took care of his younger brother who gallantly battled cerebral palsy. Though Eddie died at the tender age of 30, it was through Jim's relationship with his brother that I learned the meaning of unconditional love.

A short time after Jim and I exchanged our wedding vows the

two of us decided to start a family of our own. In the fall of 1969, I gave birth to a beautiful baby girl. Tracey made us so proud. Today our little girl is happily married. Her husband Tom is like a son to Jim and me. They have a beautiful son named Jake Thomas Bentz. We are all very close.

All of us have dreams and mine came true. I own my own business. Successful people have the ability to organize. They also set a goal and work to achieve it. The combination tends to develop an aura of confidence. Like my mother who knew exactly how much olive oil or basil to spice her sauce, my recipe for success includes faith in God, believing in yourself, and trying to always think positive. Monica, a close and dear friend, suggested the two of us attend prayer groups and Bible studies. I can't thank her enough. There is power in prayer. My faith has helped me throughout my marriage and in business deals.

I opened my own hair salon at the age of 29. My dad, who I have been very close to, was stunned at my good fortune. At times, his old school beliefs made it difficult for him to grasp this idea that his daughter could run a business. My hair salon employs a dozen people to accommodate the traffic. Besides working six days a week, I have also worked as an instructor for the State of Connecticut. I taught hairdressing classes and promoted hair-cutting exhibitions. When I wasn't working or teaching others, I also helped run the household.

Looking back, I felt stressed and tired. I traced it to trying to do too much. I can speculate that my busy schedule caused fatigue, which contributed to my illness. Perhaps the chemicals used in my profession played a factor. Whatever caused my cancer is not important anymore. Staying healthy is all that matters. I am a survivor. Every day is a bonus to me.

Chapter 2

BEING DIAGNOSED

Trust the Lord completely; don't even trust yourself.
In everything you do, put God first and he will
Direct your efforts with success.

Proverbs 3: 46

My husband has many moles on his body. We often joke that they are God's beauty marks. The two of us, however, became concerned once we learned that a good friend of ours had died from melanoma, which is a form of skin cancer. "Jim," I said, "maybe you should schedule a physical."

At the time, our family doctor, Dr. Alfonsi, who was also a surgeon, suggested some of Jim's moles should be surgically removed. In our conversations, I mentioned to the doctor that I was feeling tired all the time. I also had noticed changes to my facial features. His quick medical opinion focused at my neck. He said my glands were a bit swollen and gave me a prescription.

Jim continued to see Dr. Alfonsi. He had several of the raisin-sized moles removed from his back and chest areas. At each visit I continued to accompany my husband. It may have been a couple of months later at one of Jim's check-ups our doctor noticed my chin had enlarged. He was concerned. He suggested an ear, nose and throat specialist should examine the swelling.

I made an appointment with a specialist and underwent a biopsy. A week later I went to see the specialist. As he removed my bandage, he started to tell me that I had symptoms of lymphoma. I had heard the word before, but I had no idea what it was. I expressed no opinion. The doctor asked me to join him in his office. It was lunchtime. As the doctor ate a sandwich, he continued to talk to me about lymphoma, a form of treatable cancer, depending what kind you have. He suggested I needed to see an oncologist, a doctor who specializes in tumors.

The more the doctor talked, anger became my emotion. Maybe the doctor tried to ease my fears by nonchalantly talking about lymphoma as he ate his ham and cheese sandwich. All I could see was the doctor eating his lunch while blabbing away about lymphoma like it was a bee sting, and I could take a couple of aspirin and the swelling would go away by morning. I was filled with rage and loneliness. Why did the doctor ask me to come to his office alone? If he knew the seriousness of my tumor, you would think he would have suggested that my husband be at my side. I'm sure if he had been diagnosed his spouse would have been there. What nerve!

When I left the doctor's office, I was in a daze. I kept hearing the doctor's words echoing in my mind "your life will change as of today." It was as if I were in a trance. I got into my car and began driving. I turned the streets of Southington into my own motor speedway. I kept thinking I have cancer.

I really wanted to talk to someone...especially my husband. I remember it was early afternoon. Jim would not be home for at least three hours. My sister, an elementary school teacher, was still in class. I drove by my salon. I saw that the parking lot was filled, so I kept driving.

Don't ask why but I wound up in the neighborhood where I grew up. They say you often go back to your roots for comfort. I stopped at my parents' house.

A Touch of Peace

When I walked into the house I grew up in, my father was sitting alone at the dinner table. I usually stand when I talk and quickly began to tell my dad what I had learned from the doctor. He just sat there. He was stunned. There was concern on his face. I saw him swallow hard a couple of times. I don't remember much more. The last thing I recall was walking towards him.

When I woke up, I was lying on a sofa in the parlor. There was a wet towel on my forehead. My father was right by my side. He told me I had fainted. He had jumped out of his chair and caught me before I hit the kitchen floor.

My mother and I, circa 1945

Amazingly, a touch of peace came over me. The warm, calm feeling stayed for a few minutes. I sensed at this early stage God's presence was in the room. Everything would be all right. I looked at my father, a man to whom I felt very close all my life. I told him not to worry. I told my father to come to my house after supper and I returned home.

All of a sudden I found strength. My inner peace made me feel safe and content. I was no longer in a trance. I turned on the radio in my car. The music only added to my change in mood. I reached my home, parked the car, unlocked the door of the house and found a seat near the kitchen table.

The phone rang. It was my sister Patty. She was concerned about my appointment with the doctor. I explained to her what I had learned. Immediately, she was on her way to see me.

My sister called a cousin, a registered nurse. Joanne had considerable knowledge about various illnesses. She also had a way to reassure any patient. She also came to the house.

Together, we visited.

A short time later, Monica, my best friend, arrived.

My Detour 5

Jim and I as newlyweds. The date is September 4, 1967.

We all talked about my cancer.

Together we all cried.

The tears never seemed to stop.

Eventually the back door to my house opened. I saw my husband smile as he entered our house. I ran towards him. We met near the staircase in our living room.

I looked in my husband's eyes as if I had taken my last breath.

Jim saw the streams of water falling from my eyes.

I told Jim the doctor said that I had cancer. I had to see an oncologist.

Jim gave me a hug. Rosemary, he said, "We'll get through it."

The two of us have walked many miles together. We walked toward the kitchen arm-in-arm.

On this day our longest journey began. With God as our guide, the two of us felt we could overcome any detours on the road ahead.

Chapter 3

NON-HODGKIN'S LYMPHOMA

So don't be anxious about tomorrow.
God will take care of tomorrow, too.
Live one day at a time.

Matthew 6: 34

Previous to my diagnosis, we had never talked about cancer in our house. We talked about diabetes or heart trouble, but the only time cancer was discussed was if my girlfriend, Monica, brought it up. Her mom had died of cancer very young. For me to be diagnosed with cancer was a shock. Here I was 39. Not old by any means.

The very next day, Jim and I went to meet a hemotology oncologist. He had a stoic personality. He was more professional than personable. The subject was Non-Hodgkin's Lymphoma.

Lymphoma is cancer of the lymphatic system. The most common type of lymphoma is called Hodgkin's disease. All other forms are grouped together and are called Non-Hodgkin's Lymphoma, which is more serious than the condition known as Hodgkin's Disease.

The lymphatic system is part of the body's immune defense system. Its job is to help fight diseases and infections. Clusters of lymph nodes are found in the underarms, groin, neck, chest and abdomen area. Other parts of the lymphatic system are found in the spleen, thymus gland, tonsils, and bone marrow.

My lymphoma was found in my neck area. It was a painless swelling in the lymph node in my neck. The symptoms usually are fevers, night sweats, tiredness, weight loss, itching, and reddened patches on the skin. I never had any of these characteristics. I often felt tired, but I related my fatigue to work.

There are at least 10 types of Non-Hodgkin's Lymphoma. They are grouped into three categories by how fast they grow: low grade (slow growing), intermediate grade, and high grade (rapidly growing). With the completion of many tests, I was diagnosed with low-grade (slow growing) Non-Hodgkin's Lymphoma. Because it was slow growing and I had no symptoms, the oncologist wasn't going to treat me at this time. I wasn't content with this decision. It's like having a cold, you expect to take medicine for it and you get better.

My lymphoma wasn't that easy. Cancer responds better when it is growing fast. My lymphoma seemed to be stable. I remember my oncologist saying, "This is the best cancer you can have because it grows slowly." I laughed to myself and thought that the best kind is none at all.

A couple of months passed, and I noticed the lump in my neck was growing bigger to the point where it was bothering me. Finally, about nine months after diagnosis, my oncologist decided to give me chemotherapy. He explained different types of drugs (chemotherapy) to me and asked me "When do you want to start?"

I needed time to think. My parents went to Florida every winter. I decided to go to Florida myself. I needed to be alone to explore my feelings. I gave my husband a good-bye kiss at the airport. I wondered what he was thinking. He was such a good listener. He never said too much. I love him dearly.

As I sat on the plane, I began reading a book. A woman sitting next to me noticed the title and struck up a conversation. Come to find out, she was a nun and was not wearing a habit so I didn't recognize her vocation. She smiled. We talked and she convinced me God would always be there for me. I felt very confident. My plane ride was reassuring.

I was happy to get to Florida and to see my parents. My mother was a little confused. She was unable to remember. I missed not having my mom to hug me. She was just beginning to show visible signs of Alzheimer's Disease. Dad, meanwhile, was his usual happy self. He was ready to make a successful week for me. He often dropped me off at the beach because it was too hot for them to sit there all day. He would come late in the day and pick me up.

One particular day I was alone at the beach. I put my blanket

My mom in Florida, enjoying life.

loser to the boardwalk instead of near the water so that I could easily find it when I walked away. As I lied on my blanket, I started to write my husband a letter. I couldn't think, so I started to talk to God and asked him, "What is going on in my life?" "Did I do something wrong?" "Was I so bad that I had to get cancer?" Tears came to my eyes. Just then a little girl walked up to my blanket. She was about four feet tall, with blond curly hair and a soft voice. She handed me a religious pamphlet. It had a large Rose on the cover and the title was: **"God loves you, you are unique."** I opened the pamphlet and started to read it. The article told me how much God loved me. It told me how special I was. I knew right away the pamphlet was special and so was the little girl who gave it to me. I quickly looked up. I stood up and looked all around for this little girl. The beach was crowded with people. The boardwalk was crowded with people, but the little girl was not there. I looked for her parents or a group from where she might have come, but there was no sight of the little girl. I sat down on the blanket and started to read the pamphlet again. I knew at that moment the little girl was an angel from heaven. She brought the message that this time in my early stage of cancer God *loved me.*

I know today as I did 14 years ago that I would always be under God's care. He was my doctor, my caretaker and my strength. would survive.

I had a great week in Florida. Although I felt sad for myself, never fell apart. I remained positive. I guess that was because believed God was always going to be with me. He continues to show me His love.

On my way home from Florida I sat next to a man on the airplane who was from Massachusetts. He saw me reading my book Once again I knew God put this man next to me because of what he said. He told me that he had Non-Hodgkin's Lymphoma for five years. He explained to me about chemotherapy, how he took his pills, and how he always asked questions. I could see a light all around him as if I were dreaming. I made a point to touch his hand to make sure he was real. He was. As the man spoke, I felt safe.

I arrived home with great hope and peace. I couldn't wait to tell Jim about my trip. At the gate, Jim and I looked for the man but couldn't find him. I knew it was time to be optimistic. I was going to start my first round of chemotherapy. I felt I would be all right.

With God's help a gift of peace was given to me in Florida Every time my thoughts focused on my detour on life's highway God was there.

Chapter 4

THE LONG ROAD AHEAD

God's special gift to me is knowing Him.
Faith for me isn't something you hold or see,
It is a feeling of tranquillity,
a peace you find within yourself.

R. C.

I started my chemotherapy in 1985 on the Monday after coming home from Florida. It was like a new game for me. I like competition and I treated this as a challenge. My first oncologist gave me chemotherapy in a small, cramped impersonal room that also included the nurse who was mixing chemicals at a table right next to me. Not knowing what I know today, I let him inject toxic drugs quickly and directly into my veins, without diluting the chemotherapy. At first I was on three different drugs: Cytoxan, Vincrestine, Dexamethasone, plus Prednisone. Chemotherapy continued for nine months: One week on chemotherapy and two weeks off. I waited for all the side effects the doctor told me to expect, nausea, vomiting and mouth sores. But I wasn't too sick. I felt as if I had the "flu" most of the time. I would get terrible headaches when I stopped taking Prednisone (which occurred during my second week). By the third week, I felt fine and ready to start over again on the fourth week.

During my first bout of chemotherapy, I tried to do everything that I normally did. I worked very hard at my salon because I was afraid I would lose clients. I was pushing myself. I didn't listen to my body. Today, listening to my body is my first priority.

Chemotherapy changed my personality. It made me very tired. I

sometimes took out my frustration on the people I loved. I w[as]
always angry with my husband.

Because I was a strong person, I kept a lot of pain and loneline[ss]
to myself. I was angry with Jim because he didn't talk to me abo[ut]
my cancer. I didn't realize he was suffering, too. I felt we need[ed]
professional counseling.

My daughter completed high school that year and enrolled i[n]
college. She and I often talked about my cancer, and she went t[o]
ECAP (a cancer discussion group) meetings with me. I attende[d]
those meetings for three months. It helped both of us to understan[d]
how people must deal with cancer. We became very close. I fe[lt]
okay during this time except I was very tired and dreaded th[e]
headaches associated from chemotherapy. Finally I completed thi[s]
cycle of chemotherapy.

Being off chemotherapy gave me time to enjoy Tracey at colleg[e.]
I was glad she didn't attend a school too far away. One year after m[y]
first bout of chemotherapy I found myself back on chemotherap[y]
again. This became an ongoing cycle. I went on and o[ff]
chemotherapy with one year in between each cycle for five years. [I]
kept my sanity by going to Bible studies and different religiou[s]
lectures. One special lecture was given by Reverend Edward
McLean in Hartford. His topic was entitled, "What's it all abou[t]
Alfie," a 12-week session on life with God and different ways o[f]
understanding the Catholic Church.

Every night I would pray for my health to return. Th[e]
treatments simply wore me out. My lymphoma was a slow growin[g]
cancer; but it can be treated aggressively or non-aggressively. Th[e]
oncologist wanted to treat me aggressively, yet I felt differentl[y]
sensing there was no correct way of treating my lymphoma at thi[s]
time. I began to feel restless. I felt that I needed a new approach[.]
Maybe a new doctor who understood my illness, someone wh[o]
realized every person handles this detour in life differently. What [I]
needed after six years was a new oncologist.

One day I was working in my salon and giving a client, wh[o]
happened to be a physician, a haircut. I mentioned to this docto[r]
that I was looking for a new oncologist. He suggested I contact Dr[.]
Joseph Bowen of Waterbury. He thought we would get along ver[y]
well. I made an appointment to see Dr. Bowen. As I sat in hi[s]

Dr. Bowen always put me at ease
when I felt I was losing the battle.

office I sensed a change. I saw this caring, calm, soft-spoken person, the exact opposite of my previous oncologist. I thought I was very much in control of my emotions, yet while we were talking, I began to cry. I felt silly because having been diagnosed six years earlier I should have been accustomed to talking about cancer by now. Dr. Bowen got up from his chair and he held my hand. He told me that I wouldn't be normal if I didn't cry. I felt relieved, and I knew he was the doctor for me. We continued to talk about my case, and Dr. Bowen recommended that I go to Dana-Farber Cancer Institute in Boston for a second opinion. As a result of those meetings we decided to stay off chemotherapy and to radiate the node on my neck since the rest of my body was clean of any cancerous lymph nodes. This took place in June, 1991.

Amazingly, I was able to tolerate radiation treatments better than chemotherapy. Radiation was over in a few minutes. I had treatments every day over a 30-day period. I had radiation on the right side of my neck. I drove my car to the treatments myself. I did not like being tied to the table for the radiation treatments because I had to lie perfectly still. Crazy thoughts would go through my head about radiation as I lied on the table. But I would pray and

My dad and my brother Bob

it relaxed me. I completed my last radiation treatment in 1991. I continued to see Dr. Bowen every three months, and then we moved to a six-month period of checkups. Two years later I once again had to undergo another 30-day cycle of radiation, this time in the area of my groin. I completed this without experiencing any sickness. Gratefully, I did not require either radiation or chemotherapy for an extended period of four years.

During this time I lived every day realizing I had cancer, but I enjoyed life. My blood counts continued to be good. Even though I didn't lose my hair completely, it did grow back. I became whole again.

I continued to counsel cancer patients. I got involved in the *Look Good, Feel Better Program*, and I often wondered when my cancer would come back if ever.

During this period, my daughter graduated from college and got married in 1992. It was a happy time. Tracey and Tom's wedding was such a wonderful time.

During this period my mother was put in a convalescent home as her Alzheimer's disease became too much of a burden for my dad. This was very traumatic for me. I felt abandoned. I cried and cried for weeks. My father took care of my mother for years. But as time passed she became more forgetful, and it became harder and harder for my father to care for her. She had a stroke and went to a convalescent home. I wanted my mother to care for me. Instead, I had to care for her.

Two of the greatest, my mother and father.

I was doing well with my illness so it was easy to visit my mother at the convalescent home, which was just five minutes from my house. I went almost every day. It took me a long time to accept this change in my life. Some days, I still have difficulty with it. Other days I know the decision was for the best. No one could take care of my mother at home.

Four years after my mother was put into a convalescent home, my father developed leukemia. He was very depressed about my mother. Being the last of the children, I spent a lot of time with him. He left his family with many loving memories.

My dad was quite the philosopher and took his time telling a story. I remember how he explained his age to me. He would say, "Life is like a clock, 12 to 12:15, life has just begun, and you go from a baby to being a teenager."

"Then" he would say, "from 12:15 to 12:30 you get married, enjoy your beautiful companion, live a good life, have children and watch them grow.

"From 12:30 to 12:45, you see your children's accomplishments, you have grandchildren, but your own life starts to slow down. From 12:45 to 1 o'clock is when we notice we are getting old. You can't golf as much. Life is coming to an end."

My dad died on July 12, 1993.

A Special Gift

Before he died God allowed my dad to teach me how to accept and understand the feelings that my husband was experiencing my illness. This became *His* special gift to me. I began to realize how helpless Jim must have felt. All he could do was show me his love. I learned through my father's pain that it wasn't easy for Jim. I understood dad's fears and pain, and I felt his loss for my mom. We shared special moments together.

Without my mom to help him, at age 81, my father had to depend on his children. Each day, Patty and I would go with him for blood transfusions. Dad ended up staying at my house during the night because he didn't want to be alone. We often sat up during the middle of the night because we both could not sleep. We would talk and talk. He told me so many stories. He would often say to me " I thought I would never die." My father was always an energetic man, until he became afflicted with cancer (a word I thought he would never accept). Before he died, my dad came to understand you don't have to die with cancer, because he saw I was so alive. Dad put up a good fight, but missing mom was just too much. After two years, his heart finally gave up. I was sad, but I accepted his death because we had shared so much. My dad lived a wonderful life. I will miss him always.

I never witnessed the death of anyone before this. Dad again taught me how special death was. No pain for him. He died at home surrounded by his children just as he wanted. When I sit alone at night in my living room where I sat with dad, I smile knowing he is there with me.

I am the one who raised the dead and gives them life again.
Anyone who believes in me, even though he dies like
anyone else, he shall live again. He is given eternal life
for believing in me and shall never perish.

John 11: 25-26

Chapter 5

STEM CELL TRANSPLANT

Wisdom is a tree of life to those who eat her fruit.
Happy is the man who keeps on eating it.
Proverbs 3: 18-19

The year 1996 was a busy year for me. I was chairperson for a team called the Connecticut Hair Fashion Committee. The group is a division of the National Cosmetology Association of Connecticut. The membership entitles you to teach courses in advance hairdressing. The National Cosmetologists Association of Connecticut chose me its 1996 "Woman of the Year".

I went to the Hairdressing Convention in Washington, DC in August, 1996. While there I noticed a lump under my arm, and I could sense this one was different. My armpit hurt. I noticed that I couldn't keep up with the group. I also felt very tired. In fact, I couldn't wait to get back home. I sensed something was wrong.

When I returned home from the convention, I immediately called Dr. Bowen, my oncologist, and made an appointment. After examining me he then said I needed a biopsy and probably a treatment called stem cell transplant. He felt this was the time in my illness to have this treatment. Again, I was off to Boston for a second opinion.

I remember my first trip to Dana-Farber Cancer Institute. I talked and talked all the way up in the car during the two-hour ride. My husband didn't say much because I believe he was in shock. I don't think he ever believed I had cancer, or maybe he just didn't want to admit it. This time it was different. We were looking for an answer about the stem cell transplant.

Here I am getting the award as "Women of the Year" with Terri Baxter.

Do we ever know what we are getting ourselves into when we make a decision? I asked myself this question as I was waiting for the doctor to explain the stem cell transplant. I was originally diagnosed with Non-Hodgkin's Lymphoma which is a slow growing cancer that could one day become aggressive.

Well, the aggressive state finally came. In my research I had read that once that aggressive stage develops a person has approximately six months to one year to live. I wondered how long did I have to live? As I sat in the examination room in Boston I asked myself "Do I have a choice?" I had come a long way. It had been 12 years when I was first diagnosed. I couldn't even say the word "cancer" or even begin to think about chemotherapy. Now I was getting myself ready for a stem cell transplant.

It's easy for anyone who has cancer to be overwhelmed. I had a friend who had Non-Hodgkin's Lymphoma. He went to Dana-Farber, too. He had always talked to me about the different doctors. He ultimately went through a bone marrow transplant because there

My salon is located on Rte. 10 in Southington, Conn.

as no option such as stem cell transplant. After leaving Boston
Dr. Bowen started me on a chemotherapy protocol called C.H.O.P.
that included four different drugs: cyclophosphamide (or Cytoxan),
vincristine, doxorubicen, and 100 grams of prednisone (for five
days). These drugs do change your senses. I experienced, for
example, a lot of hyperactivity. I also came to another detour and a
bigger challenge.

Flipping My Wig

I had three cycles of chemotherapy, on one week and off two
weeks. During my treatments I lost all my hair, eyebrows and body
hair. I felt like an outcast. My hair actually fell out in about four
days. I hated the feeling when it was falling out. In hindsight it may
have been better to have cut it off before it got all over my clothes,
bed, and shower. It was upsetting. How ironic it was for a
hairdresser to have no hair. But being a hairdresser it was easy for

me to get wigs at wholesale prices. Still I did not like wearing a wig. In the winter, it did help me keep warm, but in the summer it was very uncomfortable. I felt very ugly. However, my husband never complained.

I must have had a new wig every two months. People never knew what to say.

"Is that a new hairdo?"

"Did you change your color?"

Never once did anyone say, "Is that a wig?"

Kindness I suppose.

I wonder if it was God's way of humbling me?

At night when I went to bed, I wore a hat. My head was very cold without hair. I stayed away from mirrors. My hair started to grow back three months after the stem cell transplant was completed. I first started with fuzz, then real hair. As soon as it started to cover my head, I stopped wearing wigs.

My advice is not to get an expensive wig. Try your own hairdresser or the cancer center nearest you. I used to sell wigs at cost to my clients who had cancer.

Never wear a wig near a hot oven because it will easily burn. I know. I would forget that I was wearing a wig. I'd be baking a cake and open the oven door. The blast of heat would singe the front of the wig. The wind can easily blow off your wig, so be careful. I can remember when people tried hugging and kissing me. We would always bump heads, and I'd wonder if my wig could come loose.

One time I was at a picnic and went for a walk. My wig got caught on a low branch and came off. I didn't know if I wanted to laugh or cry. I laughed. "What next?"

During this period Jim and I had to check with our insurance carrier to see where I could go for the stem cell transplant. It is sad that in times like this, we had to let our insurance company make a decision for us. I had hoped that I could go to the University of Connecticut Medical Center, just 10 minutes from our house. My insurance carrier, however, picked Yale New Haven Hospital, about 45 minutes away. It was more a hurdle than a detour.

My "home" away from home during my treatments was here at Yale-New Haven Hospital.

Making the Decision

Personally it was easier this time to make this major decision about a stem cell transplant. My daughter was now 28 years old, married and gave me great support. Tracey was no longer a teen-ager just learning that her mother had cancer. She was a beautiful, young adult. Being an only child, she grew up very fast. Now she is my confidant and is always there for me.

My husband was also great. Jim's support was another source of confidence.

So off we went to meet the oncologist at the Yale University School of Medicine. I took a complete portfolio of my condition. I always kept copies of my medical records with me. A patient will see many physicians before being assigned a primary doctor and will also have many tests before it is determined if he or she is a candidate for the stem cell transplant. Going through the tests is not easy. The extensive exams validate the cold hard fact you have cancer. All day long my clothes were on and off. You would think that by now I would be a beautiful size 6 but God blessed me with large breasts and I am probably a tight size 14. I always looked good being a hairdresser, but like a lot of people, I like to eat. My

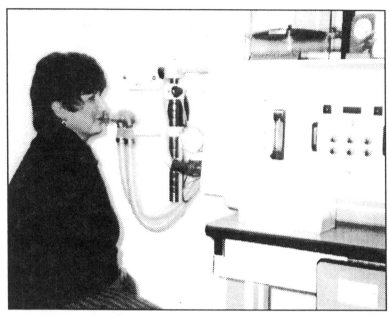

I am getting ready to take one of several exams on the
Pulmonary Function Machine.

weight was something that always concerned me, and it had to b
carefully monitored.

Having a CAT Scan no longer upset me. If I ever hear th
doctor say, "There are no more tests we can do," then I will sta
feeling afraid. I needed to have a MUGA test, which is for you
heart. It is a diagnostic exam to evaluate the motion of the hea
walls and the efficiency of the contraction and pumping of the hear
Pulmonary function tests (also called PFT) evaluate how well you
lungs are able to take in oxygen and then send that oxyge
throughout the blood stream to the rest of the body. I als
underwent a bone marrow biopsy, a very painful reminder in whic
after a local anesthetic is given, a needle is placed into your pelv
bone. A small amount of bone marrow is withdrawn through
syringe and a test is done to evaluate your bone marrow (whe
blood cells are made). It had been almost 12 years since my fir
bone marrow test, and I can still remember the piercing of th
needle. I was very much afraid because I was not complete
anesthetized. Dr. Bowen talked to me about the test. He assured m

A sense of humor never hurts. Here I am about midway through the treatments. I'm wearing an elf's cap to keep my head warm. I am also wearing my ambulatory pump.

his time he would numb the area so the test would be at least tolerable. I knew I needed this test for many medical reasons. This test would tell the oncologists many things about the stage of my cancer. I have learned that doctors all handle tests and crises differently. I trusted Dr. Bowen. The test didn't hurt this time. I was thankful.

Here's a tip. Don't be afraid to ask the doctor any question you have on your mind. Also, ask another cancer patient about his or her condition. Patients don't have the medical answers, but they tend to tell you more through their eyes and words than any doctor can.

While I underwent all those tests and made the decision to have stem cell transplant, I recalled an incident that helped me to go on. Because Therese was my confirmation name, I decided that it was time that I learned more about St. Therese, "The Little Flower." I prayed to her to help me know more about her. I thought of going to the bookstore to see if I could find some literature about St.

Therese who was canonized in 1925. I wanted to have a personal relationship with her. A week or so went by. Eventually I received Mass Card at my salon. Most Mass Cards have a picture of Jesus or the Virgin Mary on the front cover. This card was special. It was more like a little book and it had a healing prayer from St. Therese. Her mission began after she died. "She will let fall a shower of roses." God had indeed chosen her to be an instrument of his love.

The very next day a client of mine who had no idea about St. Therese and didn't know what was going on in my life at the moment surprised me. The client had just returned from a vacation trip and brought me back a pair of earrings that were in the shape of roses.

I continue to pray each day to St. Therese. There's not a week that goes by that I don't see roses. *Every day I see samples of St. Therese's love for me.* I know I am in God's hands throughout the stem cell transplant procedure and can solve my detour. Thank you St. Therese.

This photo with my mother is after my chemotherapy had ended. My hair is beginning to return.

Chapter 6

MEETING DR. COOPER

*Listen to me! You can pray for anything
and if you believe, you have it. It's yours.*
Mark 11: 24

I met Dr. Dennis Cooper, MD, and Clinical Director of the stem cell transplant program at Yale New Haven Hospital. The hospital at Yale is a teaching hospital, and there are many interns asking almost the same questions. After the interns it was time to meet Dr. Cooper a man whom I learned to admire. I was excited and frightened, but Dr. Cooper entered the room with a warm greeting and an easy smile. He had such an approachable manner about him. His smile seemed to come as much from his eyes as from his mouth. He was very calm as he spoke. Immediately I felt confident with him and his decisions.

Betsey D'Andrea, the coordinator nurse for the stem cell unit, reviewed the paperwork with me. I could tell she was a resourceful and intelligent person. Her level of confidence made me feel as if I were in good hands. She didn't push me to make quick decisions. She explained in detail what a stem cell transplant involved. She also played a big role in my stem cell transplant and recovery.

I asked Betsey what a stem cell was, and she said, "A stem cell is the mother cell of all cells in blood, a cell that can manufacture red cells, white cells, and platelets and gives them the ability to multiply. They are good healthy cells."

I went away from the meeting feeling very optimistic. I had trust in the program. Once again I believed in the power of prayer. I felt the presence of God was very important to my recovery. I kept thinking, "He will get me through this."

In the early years of my illness I was afraid. It was different now. I knew this treatment had to be done. I realized it was a life-threatening treatment, but I was prepared. I had handled chemotherapy four different times and radiation twice. I had been weak many times throughout my years with cancer yet I learned how to take it "one day at a time." So that evening at Yale in Dr. Cooper's office I signed the papers for the stem cell transplant. It was official. I was going to have a transplant. My decision caught my husband and daughter off guard. They wanted me to take the papers home, read them over and come to a decision in a couple of days. But I didn't want anyone but me to have this responsibility. If I died, I didn't want my family to blame themselves. It was my decision.

I just knew I could do it even though I didn't know what each day would bring.

On Nov. 25, 1996, I signed the consent form. A week from that day I would start my CD34+ Cells from Mobilized Stem Cell Collections for Hematological Rescue of Patients or the Stem Cell Transplant.

That evening, I lay very close to Jim in our bed. I couldn't sleep. I wondered if this procedure was okay for me. I started to talk to my dad in heaven. I needed him so much at this time that I even had a dream about him. I woke up from that dream feeling good. I sensed my dad was near me. This was the moment that God had prepared me for. My cousin's husband gave me a religious scapular to wear. I took it to Yale with me and wore it all the way through the stem cell transplant.

My treatments started on December 3, 1996. My strong awareness of God's presence had been with me many years before that December day at Yale. It was clear to me that everything that had happened before this moment was just preparation.

I felt like a fighter who trained for the big fight. I had read many books on being positive. I had asked all the questions. I was ready for any detours ahead.

Chapter 7

THE HOSPITAL

Anyone who wants to come to God must
Believe that there is a God and that
He rewards those who sincerely look for Him.

Hebrews 11: 6

I remember December 3, 1996, quite vividly. Jim, Tracey and I went to Yale New Haven Hospital to begin my stem cell transplant. My first task was to have an intravenous catheter surgically implanted in a large vein in my chest. This device, also called a portacath, would be used in chemotherapy to take drugs, give fluids, blood products, and to draw blood. Inside the portacath are two chambers or "lumens." The installation of this catheter involved a surgical procedure. I did not know what to expect as I waited in the Radiology Department at Yale. I was taken to an operating room. Although it is a minor outpatient operation, doctors and nurses always had trouble finding my veins. I would normally have to endure three or four "sticks" with a needle, because my vein rolled. Having the catheter installed meant that I would have no more needles in my arms.

I finally got into the operating room. The room was small and cold. You don't wear much clothing just a "johnny" coat. They are thin and most of the time they never fit. This was one of those times when I wished I had small breasts because as I lay on the bed in the operating room they had to tape my breasts so that they wouldn't get in the way. I was awake during the procedure. A nurse took a test of my heart to see if it was okay. Then I was given local anesthesia. The nurse told me to look at her while the doctors were placing the portacath in my chest. Because Yale New Haven Hospital is a medical teaching school, I could hear one of the surgeons explaining the procedure to an intern. I was relaxed. I prayed before the procedure and trusted in God to walk with me. I was anxious to get this over with. I realized I was talking a lot to the

My festive holiday attire was not complete without my ambulatory pump. That's Champ on my right.

nurse but I can't remember what I said. Everyone was very nice, and it was soon over.

"Sit up," said the nurse," You can go out and get dressed." I couldn't believe I could just sit up and go. I didn't feel anything, at least at this moment. Off I went down the hallway to find my family. Like always when I saw my husband I started to cry.

The Journey Begins

To think this was the first couple of hours of a very long procedure was a little unsettling. I am always brave in front of the people I don't know, but with my family, it's a different story. Jim is my pillow and I can lean on him any time. He and my daughter both gave me the strength to go on. I may cry for a moment, but quickly move on. I thank God for that gift.

Next stop was a private room in the Oncology Unit, the 8th floor of the Yale Children's Hospital in New Haven. It is across the street from the Oncology Clinic in the Yale Physicians Building where I went for blood work and chemotherapy.

The hospital room was not unpleasant. It contained a couch that allowed Jim to stay overnight. It also had a TV, clock and a bathroom. It would be home for a few days so I did my best not to feel claustrophobic. I was in the hospital to receive IV fluids and chemotherapy over the next several days. I had to receive anti-nausea medication as well. All of these would be administered through my portacath.

In a few days I noticed other patients and realized we all looked alike – no hair, no eyebrows. We were basically restricted to the room. Only immediate family could visit. No flowers, no fruit, no lettuce. They all carry parasites. As the first day passed, the nurses came with my IV fluids. Later that night I would receive my first dose of chemotherapy.

Even though I had been undergoing chemotherapy for over three months, I knew this dosage would be much stronger. I was ready for the challenge. The fluids caused my legs to swell. I gained 10 pounds from the fluid. Then the chemotherapy started, and they injected it right through the portacath. I braced for the side effects: the nausea, vomiting, diarrhea, mouth sores, skin rashes, loss of appetite, fatigue, and the unpleasant taste in my mouth.

A Real Roadblock

The first dose of chemotherapy is called "mobilizing." It lasts four days. This procedure is used to destroy as many cancer cells as possible. It also helps the bone marrow to release stem cells into the blood stream. At the same time the treatments slow down the production of white cells, red cells, and platelets made in bone marrow. My blood was drawn three times a week. It was also checked daily for blood counts. The people at Yale were always watching my platelet count so I wouldn't have bleeding. Chemotherapy does make the white blood cells and platelet counts drop to low levels. Because of this, a patient is at high risk for infection. If I developed a fever when I left the hospital, I would be immediately re-hospitalized. Once the bone marrow recovers and the number of white cells in the blood increases, the stem cells could be collected, or "harvested." A process called apheresis does this. It also means you are on the road to recovery.

My husband and daughter were supportive during this time. They also didn't say too much. Jim took a lot of time off from work, and it really drained him. My love for him grew stronger. I noticed that his hair got grayer throughout this ordeal. Many nights he slept at the hospital on a small couch next to my bed. It was good having him near me. The next day about noon he would go home. Then my daughter Tracey would come. Tracey works as a

my daughter Tracey

paralegal. Her company granted her a leave of absence. She also worked from her home at night by means of a direct line computer connection to her office.

In the months leading up to my transplant, Tracey had a miscarriage. I felt so sorry for her because I knew she had been trying to have a baby. If she were pregnant, it probably would have been stressful for both of us. I tried to comfort her as mothers do. I always protected Tracey. Maybe it wasn't time for her to have a baby. God knows what he is doing. Someday she will be a mother. I prayed for this every night. I wanted her to know the joys of being a mother as I do.

Chapter 8

CHEMO - DAY 2

He forgave all my sins. He heals them.
He ransomed me from hell.
He surrounds me with loving kindness
and tender mercies.

Psalms 103: 3-5

I remained in the hospital for four days. Every hour felt different. Time went by slowly. The nights were very lonely. One day would bring sadness and loneliness. Another day my emotions were isolation and fear. The following day I would feel confident and ready to go on. The mind can sometimes take much longer to recover than the body. I once read a book by Gilda Radner, **"It's Always Something."** Eventually this wonderful person lost the battle from ovarian cancer. She explained her chemotherapy as feeling nauseous for about nine months. When it was over, she gave birth to herself. I carried that thought with me every time I had treatment. I felt that when my chemotherapy had ended, I created myself a new life. I know when this stem cell transplant is over, I will be a new person.

My portacath was a discomfort. I was allergic to the tape they used on me. Each time I got up I could feel the muscles in my chest pulling. Still I often wondered why the portacath was put in two or three days before I started chemotherapy. Simple things like getting up and down hurt my chest. But as time passed, I learned to accept it.

My best friend Monica. The two of us have been buddies for over 30 years.

Chapter 9

NEUPOGEN

He fills me with strength and protects me wherever I go.
Psalm 18: 32

Days three and four in the hospital were better. I continued to get chemotherapy. I looked forward to the next phase even though I didn't know what to expect. When I finally got home from the hospital, I waited for an IV Visiting Nurse to come and explain what the next steps would be. I had one day off from all medication.

My next task was to learn how to give myself a needle so that I could inject myself with a medicine called Neupogen. This drug is a protein that stimulates your bone marrow to make lots of white cells. To speed up the recovery I needed to increase my white blood cell count and the number of stem cells in the blood stream. Neupogen signals the bone marrow to produce white cells. The theory is the increased number of white cells will make the marrow expand and force the white cells particularly the increased stem cells to circulate in your blood. That may be true, but I also felt the treatments left me with bone pain and fatigue. There were other symptoms too. My pain continued until after my stem cell transplant.

Jim and I became nurses. We learned a number of things about self-injection. Giving myself a needle was a challenge. I had the choice of arm or leg, and I had to learn to release the Neupogen very slowly to avoid intense burning. It took us about three days to get it right.

When I was home alone, I would cry thinking of what was going on. As the days passed the needles became a little less painful. Jim and I had to learn how to clean the portacath. It had two lumens. I would use one side one day and the other side the next day. We taped little numbers on them so we wouldn't lose track of where we were. In the daily flushing of the lumens, we used Heparin and saline solution. We seemed to have it down to a science after a while. The visiting nurses from the Home Care Agency kept an ample supply of dressings and caps. They experimented and found materials that wouldn't irritate my skin. The attending nurses were great.

Here I am dressed for a holiday party and wearing my ambulatory pump.

Chapter 10

THE CLINIC

A man's goodness helps him all through life,
while evil men are being destroyed by their wickedness.
Proverbs 13:6

I'd often hear traffic reports on the radio when the commentator would warn motorists about the daily hazards of commuting to work. At times it's downright torture. How does anyone ever get to the office on time? Connecticut may be a small state, but the roads are well traveled. My daily trips to New Haven for transfusions and blood tests became a routine. We would leave at 6:45 a.m. and arrive by 7:30 a.m. Jim drove. We talked. We held hands. He was as much a traveler on the journey as I was.

The clinic was a large room with about 25 chairs. There were recliners with TVs nearby and maybe four beds complete with curtains for those who could not sit in chairs. This room became my "home" away from home except on weekends when I had to go to the eighth floor of the Yale Children's Hospital (which is where the Oncology Unit was located). I would get blood transfusions. The nurses would first test me to see what my blood counts were. It took about one hour before I knew the results of the test. If I needed blood or platelets it would take close to four hours. Jim would go home and then my daughter would pick me up. Every day when I got home I was very tired, so I took some nausea pills and tried to sleep.

While at the clinic I would often talk to people. My nature is to be friendly. I guess that is part of my personality. I have to talk to someone just to let him or her know someone cares. Inside of me I really felt sad for them, and there were times when I wanted to cry. I

Three people of many who were supportive during my ordeal are featured here: R.N. Joanne Ascione and my sisters, Susan Belanger and Patty Sgrillo.

could feel their pain and see the fear in their eyes. After all we were going through the same thing. Some days I went home sad, other days I felt okay. I prayed that we all would make it. Each day was a new day.

My blood was checked every day of the week, and the people at the clinic kept a close watch on all of us. Each time I went to the clinic, Dana, my personal nurse, would care for me by taking my vital signs. This would go on each day until the procedure was over. We traveled 60 miles a day for three months.

Chapter 11

THIRD WEEK - HOSPITAL INFECTION

Jesus told him, "Go back home. Your son is healed!"
JOHN 4: 50

During my second week of treatments I arrived for a blood test. I felt very sluggish. That day the 8th floor seemed like the 80th floor. Dr. Cooper was waiting for me. He took a look at me and said that I was going to be admitted to the Yale Hospital Oncology Floor. He sensed something was wrong. From day one I trusted Dr. Cooper because of his patience, kindness, and intelligence. He was correct. I had an infection from the portacath, and it was life threatening because my counts were so low. I remained in the hospital for four days. I was upset yet thankful that Dr. Cooper found my problem. I was extremely tired, and I slept most of the time thinking that maybe this is how I should feel. It only had been two weeks, and I found myself back in the hospital. The days were very long. Every day I wondered what was going to happen next.

It was Christmas time, and I could see the Christmas decorations and hear the Christmas music. On this day I heard a choir singing. I walked out into the hallway and noticed the children were from a school. This scene reminded me of my mother who has Alzheimer's Disease and lives in a convalescent home. I was thinking how she never knew I had an illness. I felt I was as helpless as she was. I quickly went back into my room. I didn't want anyone to see me. I felt old and having lost my hair made me look like an alien. I started to cry. I wondered when my nightmare would be over. Here I was just starting, and I knew I had a long way to go. I am happy I have my family. It seemed every time I was lonely, the phone rang. It was my sister Susan. She lives out of state. Patty, my other sister, would visit me often. After four days,

Here I am with two great friends, Dolores and Monica.

Dr. Cooper decided I could go home. I had to wear an ambulatory pump for four weeks. An IV nurse came to my house and taught Jim and I how to operate it. It was a battery powered pump that I wore on my waist and it was connected to my portacath. It pumped antibiotics into my system every six hours, which took one hour. Sleeping was difficult with the pump. I was able to carefully bathe with the device attached, and it became a part of me. It was about the size of a small pocketbook. Jim and I had many jobs: Cleaning the ports on the portacath, giving myself injections of Neupogen, and setting my ambulatory pump each day.

I like challenges but I could not comprehend what was going on in my body. I just took one day at a time. I prayed every moment I could and trusted God to get me through this ordeal.

Finally, the time came to suspend giving myself Neupogen shots for a while. The next phase was apheresis, a procedure that is performed to collect stem cells in a process very similar to dialysis.

I was doing better. I was half way through my treatments. Would there be more detours to challenge me?

Chapter 12

APHERESIS: Collecting Stem Cells

Jesus told him, "I am the way,
and the truth and the life.
No one can get to the Father
except by means of me."
John 14: 6

Apheresis is a process that takes three to four hours. In order to collect stem cells a quentin catheter was used. The procedure, though not painful, was very tiring. The blood is being separated into components by an apparatus that resembles a dialysis machine. The nurses used my quentin catheter to collect my stem cells that are found in the white blood cells. It was very hard to sit there for three to four hours. I got to the Apheresis Center around 7:30 a.m. My husband drove me to New Haven and my daughter picked me up when I was finished. I went through this process for five days.

Each time I came to the Apheresis Unit, the procedure seemed longer and longer. The room consisted of reclining chairs and two beds. Some people were there to get blood transfusions. I shared a TV with the person who sat next to me. I remembered a new talk show was on. It was called *The Rosie O'Donnell Show*. She would always make me laugh.

The nurse was very good to me, but I felt very uncomfortable trying to sit perfectly still for three to four hours. The aphresis was performed through a quentin catheter that I had surgically installed in my neck. The catheter consisted of two tubes that protruded out of my neck area, just below the shoulder blade. It was a real

My sisters and brother join me in this Christmas snapshot. That's Susan, Bob, Patty and I.

nuisance, but the good thing was this would be removed after the apheresis was finished. I couldn't wait. Each day, however, I seemed to become weaker and weaker.

During these treatments my mind often wandered. I recalled as I sat in the chair thoughts of my mother-in-law who is going through dialysis three times a week. A driver picks her up each day and brings her to a Dialysis Center about 30 minutes away. She goes alone, and is on the dialysis machine for two or three hours She waits about 30 minutes after the procedure for her van ride home. She goes home to her apartment and tries to cook her own supper and fall asleep. She is 76 years old and lives alone. I don't know how she does it. My apheresis was only for a period of five days. I had a husband to come home to. I felt sad for all the people who were alone in this world. You can't put a price on companionship.

It was now Friday. Hopefully this would be my last day. Much would depend on my cell count. I could just about walk into the room by myself. I remember it was a very cold day and I wore a long winter green coat. The garment felt so heavy that I had difficulty walking. Jim wanted to get me a wheelchair but I declined. If this were going to be my last day, I was looking forward to some time off. I needed close to 2.5 million kilograms of my body weight of collected cells to complete the stem cell transplant. I did not want to go through this another day. I was praying the procedure would be over because the cramping in my legs was getting unbearable. I was very tired. Dr. Cooper came to the unit, and after meeting with the nurse, it was decided that enough cells had been collected. The process was now over. I was very relieved. My stem cell collection was a success. Now the doctors would freeze these stem cells until it would be time to transplant these blood cells back into my body. This would occur once the next round of chemotherapy was complete.

When the harvesting or collection of my stem cells was over, Betsey took the tube out of my neck. I was ready to go home and rest for two weeks. This would allow the infection in my portacath to heal. Then I would return to Yale for heavy doses of chemotherapy twice a day.

So far I felt very good. I didn't think the procedure was bad. I was home for the Christmas holidays. Best of all I was off chemotherapy. My white blood count was up. I was able to be near people and join my family at my sister's house for Christmas. I really missed seeing my mother. I was thrilled to see her. She smiled at me as if she knew who I was. Who knows, maybe there was a place deep inside of her that remembered me.

Christmas was sad without my father being there. Our family celebrated as if he were. We recalled him singing Christmas carols. After being isolated for so long, I was happy to go to my sister's house for our holiday dinner. Previously no one was allowed to have any contact with me. Our house was a fortress against germs and outsiders. I loved seeing my family, my nieces, and nephews. I felt alive again.

My husband Jim and I share a special moment.

Chapter 13

THE SURPRISE

Some rich people are poor, and some poor people have great wealth!
Proverbs 13: 7

The date of January 4, 1997, had been circled on the calendar. My husband and daughter were going to throw a Benefit Dance for me. I could see in Tracey's eyes that she was excited and proud to stage this party. I really thought it was going to be a family get-together. In the event I could not attend, I made plans. I called my cousin's son-in-law, and since he runs a company that converts photographs into VHS format, I thought I would surprise my daughter and my husband to turn our extensive collection of pictures into a video with music. It was a collage of 30 years together. I wanted my husband Jim to have something special from me in case I didn't make it through the stem cell.

During my two weeks of recuperation, I could sense I was regaining my strength. I wanted to go to the party. My family was afraid to have me go because of the possibility of catching a cold or an infection from people in attendance. A couple of days before the party I had an appointment at the oncology clinic to have my blood counts checked. I was happy to hear the doctor tell me that it was safe to be around people. My counts were good. I considered myself very lucky.

The big night finally arrived. Jim, Tracey, and her husband Tom went to the hall first to greet all the people. I didn't want to go early or stay late so I waited until Jim came to get me. I found out later

*My hair is beginning to grow back as Jim and
I celebrate our 30th wedding anniversary.*

that Jim had announced at the hall that he was going to get me, and
he cautioned everyone who might have a cold to keep their distance.
Jim came to get me around 7:30 p.m. It was very exciting to think
that I would be around all my close friends. Being Italian and
having a large extended family on both my parents' side and many
clients from 30 years of business, I knew a lot of people would be
there. I also had my surprise, the VHS presentation. Even though I
thought people other than my family would be there, I wondered if
it would be tacky to show the cassette.

Well, I walked into this very beautiful banquet hall and there
were over 500 people waiting for me. My family, friends, clients,
politicians, my special family at work, and just so many people. I
was overwhelmed with the love everyone was showing. There were
people in attendance I didn't even know, but they had come to
support me. Many others had sent cards and flowers. Many of my
clients made cookies. We had plenty to eat. My family, my sisters,
friends and cousins all worked with my daughter Tracey, the great
organizer, and her husband Tom to put this together.

The Tarantino family in 1952: dad, mom, my brother and me between my sisters in the front row.

The VHS presentation went off well. There were plenty of tears of happiness shed. I felt that the video presentation expressed my love to my family and friends, especially for my husband and daughter. A friend of mine, who is a Catholic Deacon, gave a wonderful spiritual reading. I spent the evening trying to talk to everyone who attended. It was a night *I will never forget.* Feeling very tired on this night was a good feeling. I only wished my dad could have been there. He would have been so proud of his whole family and me. It was sad to see the night come to an end.

I continued to receive get well cards for several weeks after the Benefit Dance. I knew the next few months were not going to be easy, but with the whole town praying for me, how could anything go wrong?

Here I am with two good friends who helped give me support during my ordeal: Lynette Testa (center) and Joyce Sieracki (right).

Chapter 14

ANOTHER CHALLENGE

Gentle words cause life and health;
griping brings discouragement.

Proverbs 15: 4

My next hurdle was to complete six consecutive days of high dose chemotherapy. I was starting to understand a stem cell transplant is not the treatment for cancer. The high dose chemotherapy was to kill my cancer cells. The stem cells given back to me rebuild the bone marrow that had been destroyed by the very high doses of chemotherapy. At this time I would also be going back on the Neupogen injections, a protein that stimulates bone marrow so that it can produce white cells. The medical staff knew exactly what to do. I was amazed how the nurses and doctors worked in unison to make this program a success. The Home Care Agency also employed one of the nurses who worked during the day at Yale, (at the Oncology Inpatient Unit), and she gave me chemotherapy in the evening at my home. I would go to the oncology clinic at around 7:30 a.m., and Dana would give me chemotherapy. The process took about four hours. Then I would receive chemotherapy at home 12 hours after the morning dosage.

It was during one of these drives to New Haven that I noticed all the cars going by on the Interstate, and I wondered if these motorists had any family problems. Only a person in a caring family understands what this ordeal is like. No one really knows who is having a problem or what is going on in other people's lives? I really believe in the philosophy of one day at a time. If I were sick, I would try to sleep, take a hot bath, or buy some flowers. Sometimes I would play music. I used to feel guilty about being selfish, but not anymore. Time is very important to me.

When the nurse came to my house in the evening, I was already sick from my morning chemotherapy treatment. But the nausea medicine, Adavan, helped me. I took the evening chemotherapy in my own bed and being home was a relief. Each treatment, however, would seem like a very long time, and my legs would cramp terribly at night. The nights were very long. The chemotherapy left me with an unpleasant taste in my mouth. I often would munch on sourball candies just to counter the tin taste. I would also drink lemonade. That made my mouth feel better and my tastebuds seem almost normal. As for food macaroni and ice cream never tasted so good.

Chapter 15

OFFICER AND A GENTLEMAN

We can make our plans,
but the final outcome is in God's hands.
Proverbs 16: 1

During my treatment this one particular day I felt extremely tired. I needed blood and platelets. While I was sitting in the reclining chair waiting for chemotherapy, I told Dana, my clinic nurse, that I felt sick. She took my blood pressure and called for my doctor. Dr. Cooper is a medium frame man, about 5-foot-11. He asked me to walk over to one of the beds so he could examine me. As I walked over to the bed, I'm told I fainted because the nurses said that Dr. Cooper had scooped me up in his arms and placed me softly on the bed. I felt embarrassed. I wondered how he could have picked me up so fast. He smiled and said, "Don't worry, just call me an officer and a gentleman." Never once did Dr. Cooper lose his sense of humor. He smiled at me again, and while reading my thermometer, he realized that my high fever could be better treated in the oncology unit. This decision was difficult, but it was for the best. I would now get chemotherapy and Neupogen at the hospital.

I always carried a suitcase and my pillow with me in the car just in case I would have to be admitted which was becoming a habit. So it was back in Yale New Haven Hospital. I was hoping the time would pass quickly, but I stayed four days. When Sunday morning arrived, a nurse took me to mass in the church because I hadn't been for a long time and I missed it. What a sight I was! Here I was in a wheelchair, wearing a surgical mask with my medicine bags

That's Dr. Cooper on my right. This man helped me understand what stem cell transplant is all about and I am grateful for his kindness and encouragement during my time of illness.

hanging over my head. I felt very self-conscious and couldn't wait to get back to my room.

I spent the rest of the day in my room until I was ready to be dismissed. I saw Dr. Cooper and pleaded with him to send me home. My temperature was normal, but he said that I had to have blood and platelets before I could be discharged. As I received new plasma and platelets, I wondered whose blood I was getting. It was kind of scary thinking about these transfusions, but I just had to trust God. I very seldom tried to analyze the procedures I was going through. I did worry, but when I felt my body tighten with anxiety, I calmed myself by reading or saying a prayer. I was coming to the end of my stem cell procedure. With one week to go, I felt very tired and sick from the treatments. My husband often lay next to me on the hospital bed. I enjoyed the comfort of him hugging me. I am glad he realized this was a problem for both of us. A short time later I was discharged from the hospital.

Chapter 16

RECEIVING MY STEM CELLS

The wise man looks ahead.
The fool attempts to fool himself and won't face facts.
Proverbs 14: 8

The chemotherapy was finally over. I was receiving my stem cells back into my body, and I went alone to the clinic because I didn't expect any difficulty. Betsey was the nurse who would perform the procedure through my portacath.

I don't remember being nervous, yet my body seemed to be playing a trick. My legs kept shaking. I couldn't sit still. I was fine when Betsey gave me intravenous fluids, but the infusion of my stem cells was different. The nurse watched me carefully for several minutes. I felt no pain. I was excited and happy to know the treatment was over. Receiving the stem cells was easy. It took about 10 minutes. Now I had to wait until the cells reached my bone marrow and started to grow. Only then would I have a healthy body again.

During the critical time following the stem cell transplant, I had to have my blood levels checked daily. The medication was prescribed to prevent infection Cipro (an antibiotic), Diflucan (an anti-fungal) and Zoviraz (an anti-viral).

I felt very good; a new body was to be born.

I was ready to travel down the highway. Would there be any more detours?

I wrote this book during a number of get-aways to Newport, Rhode Island.

Chapter 17

ENGRAFTMENT

Was God being unfair? Of course not.
For God has said to Moses,
"If I want to be kind to someone, I will.
And I will take pity on anyone I want to."
Romans 9: 14-15

Engraftment is when the new stem cells start to grow independently. During the time the marrow is being rebuilt, the white blood cell count, red blood cell count and platelet count are usually at low numbers because of the high doses of chemotherapy. Red blood cell transfusions are designed to improve the circulation of oxygen to all parts of the body. The platelet transfusions are vital to help the blood clot.

It often takes a week to 10 days for the process to show results. Within days Dana, my nurse, noticed my white cell count began to grow. My recovery had started.

The daily trips to the clinic each morning to check my blood were no longer a bother. Neither were any transfusions. By day 10, my transplant was complete. My bone marrow was working again! The stem cell transplant had taken. I was now on my way.

The doctors had told me that if the transplant succeeds, I would feel like a new person and that my strength over time would return. In the beginning, I could just about walk up 8 or 10 stairs and needed to catch my breath. Just getting around my house felt like a marathon. Some days I went to my beauty salon to visit the girls.

Members of my Hair Expo staff are featured here with me,
Stacy and Terri on my right and Alison on my left.

Within an hour my body was telling me I needed rest. Still, getting out and seeing my friends made me feel good.

I have a special woman who works for me. Her name is Joan, a massage therapist. She is my angel. Joan kept me going through my chemotherapy and radiation. From the beginning to the end of my illness, she gave me massages. It helped my recovery. I felt so relaxed. Her tender touch helped calm my body and mind. I would dream of a beautiful place and pretend I was there. Some people can read a book or watch television to relax, but how many soaps or movies can you watch? I needed tranquillity. I found it through Joan and her therapeutic touch.

Thanks, Joan.

Chapter 18

A NEW PERSON

*In everything you do, put God first
and He will direct you and crown your effort with success.*
Proverbs 3: 6-7

I sensed I was getting better when the doctors said my visits to the clinic would be every other day. My white cells and blood counts kept growing. Each day was truly a new day. As my blood counts improved, I was feeling whole again.

It was finally over when my nurse Dana told me that no more blood work was necessary.

"How do you know it's over?" I asked.

Dana told me that my blood work was very good, and my chances for complete recovery were strong. Time is a great healer. Dr. Cooper said it would take six months to a year before I started to feel like myself again.

I was amazed that my ordeal was over. I wondered how my body managed to deal with these changes. I had chemotherapy for four days. I made white cells with Neupogen. The good cells were cleaned, saved, and frozen. Then there was high dose chemotherapy twice a day. Next I received my stem cells when they were harvested (on the 7th to 10th day). Overall, this process took three months.

I am trying to understand what I have been through. So many people tell me I look good, and how great it must be to be in recovery. When I looked in the mirror, however, I saw a round fat face with no eyebrows and no eyelashes. I felt like a prisoner of war. My skin was dry. I felt very old.

My sister Susan, who lives in Saratoga, New York, came to see me. I didn't see her as much as I saw my other sister and brother. Sue said that I looked good. My family gave me so much love. My brother Bob and his wife Susan also came to see me. My brother was quiet throughout the whole ordeal. He reminded me of my dad. The thing to realize is that treatment isn't easy for anyone especially relatives of the family. I saw the love in Bob's eyes, and I would call to reassure him that I was okay. It was difficult for all of us. I have so many people to thank. Those people made this procedure a little easier. I love them all.

I have a new feeling about life. I see everything better. I worried whether I will ever get my energy back and get back to work. I was fortunate to have a great team at my place of business. The girls kept my hair salon going.

Several years ago when I was going through chemotherapy, I almost lost my business. Several faithful workers, some who had put in close to 15 years of service, decided to leave. Starting over again wasn't easy. My cousin Donna, who was also a hairdresser, came to the rescue. She helped me keep the business going. With the grace of God, my current staff has kept the salon running and has remained dedicated to my clients and me. I will always be grateful. I do worry about becoming too dependent on them, but I need time to recuperate. The valuable lesson learned through this detour is that we all need each other. We cannot walk this road of life alone.

Within three months my hair started to grow back. I had thin hair before, but now it was curly and full. I started to look and feel like a woman again. My mood started to lift a little. There was progress each day, but there was also a degree of depression. It does take a long time for the mind to catch up with the body. My emotions were something I had to solve. Feelings of sadness and loneliness, isolation, and fear were mind games I had to deal with. I believed I would fully recover, but it is difficult to ease the trauma of my disease. Stem cell transplant changed my life.

I am a survivor. I met adversity. With support of my family, friends, and personal talk through prayer with my creator, I believe I am cancer free. I can handle any detour that comes in my path.

Chapter 19

AFTER STEM CELLS

Those who believe him discover that God is a fountain of truth.
John 3: 33

I have often heard my husband talk about athletes who have played sports with pain. Take pro football for example. The nature of the game lends itself to collisions. It's amazing more players don't get severely hurt or paralyzed.

I wonder what type of pain these players must battle through the day after playing a game?

I wonder what type of disability some must live with once they exit the game?

To a degree, I think I know.

About a month after my treatment ended, I had severe bouts of pain. It was like I had been mugged. I had aches in my stomach, neck and spine. I had leg cramps. To ease the pains I took hot baths. This helped me to sleep. Many times my husband woke up and found me in the tub. Jim finally convinced me to call my family doctor Dr. Ciardella.

At first Dr. Ciardella concluded my pain was pleurisy. A visit to a pulmonary specialist confirmed it was not a condition of my lungs. So the next step was to undergo a bone scan.

Up to this point I thought everything was under control. Immediately the thought of more chemotherapy put me on edge. I lost control of my senses. I felt helpless. I couldn't eat, think, or talk. I just wanted to be alone. I often said a prayer. I believe in the power of prayer. Many times the verses calmed my mind. You must have faith that your prayers will be answered.

Dr. Ciardella always found time in his busy day to answer any question I had concerning my illness.

Dr. Bowen, who had been my oncologist for the past eigh years, ran into my cousin, Judy, a nurse who works at the sam hospital in Waterbury, CT. She told him about my bone pain an Dr. Bowen suggested I call him and make an appointment. Since was under the care of Dr. Cooper at Yale, I wasn't sure what to dc I decided to see Dr. Bowen. He explained to me that many of hi other patients who had a stem cell transplant also had bone pair much like arthritis. Dr. Bowen prescribed aridea, a medication fo treating bones. This helped the calcium in my bones and also easec pain. Within a few months, my bone pain had diminished.

Footnote: One of the reasons I wrote this book is to make people aware that if you do not get answers you understand from your doctors, then seek other opinions. I wonder if doctor document side effects from other clients to help all their patients When I was told I would begin to feel better within 6 months, the doctors were right. Still they did not specify about the side effect that I might feel.

Chapter 20

PEOPLE

*We are saved by trusting. And trusting means
looking forward to getting something we don't yet have.
If we must keep trusting God for something
that hasn't happened yet,
it teaches us to wait patiently and confidently.*
Romans 8: 24-25

It meant a great deal to me that people would take the time to all. My heart goes out to people who feel abandoned or don't have ith. You don't need to be told you are courageous yet, time and me again, I found inspiration through the bravery and deep faith of thers who shared battles with cancer.

My decision to discuss my cancer openly and honestly was easy. eing brave is not easy all the time. You need help. But knowing, eing, and believing in God works wonders. When I have a bad ay, I call my best friend or sister. We talk or say prayers until my ars go away. We pray with each other and know in our hearts od is with us.

Family and friends are important. Some people tell me their ved ones died of cancer, and they didn't talk about it before they ied. Everyone handles an illness in his or her own way. Do hatever works. When I was first diagnosed, I felt like I was ttending my own wake. It was overwhelming, yet I knew that eople meant well. I would tell everyone I was okay, but deep down, was in shock.

I believe group discussions help people understand any illness. I emember when I was first diagnosed, I needed to talk to someone ho had cancer because I thought I could relate to someone who ad the same illness. It was an instant bond when I first met with the "group." We could understand each other's frustrations and counseling. For a few weeks the group helped. However, I left the committee because I found the answers I needed and wanted to move on. Feeling sorry for yourself is okay, but it must be only temporary. It is natural to wonder what my life would have been like without lymphoma. I think I'm stronger because I have battled through it.

My husband and I still attend stem cell group meetings. These discussions are held every month at Yale New Haven Hospital. Betsey D'Andrea and Bonnie Indeck organize the meetings and help others understand and share their stem cell experience.

In December 1998, I attended a survivor's cancer Christmas party. It was good to see my comrades. Our families always share a special bond.

Do we ever wonder why we go through so many detours in our life?

I was asked many times, "How did you do it?"

My answer will always be, "It wasn't easy."

I don't know if it was the courage, strength, or the will to live that helped me overcome my detour. The love of my family, support from my friends, and the power of prayer helped a great deal.

Above all I believe it was my state of mind that buoyed my spirit in my times of peril.

I've always looked at the glass as being half full. That philosophy is a must in life for any relationship to work or any business deal to succeed.

A positive attitude will do wonders to control your destiny. It enabled me to conquer pain and fear. It enabled me to live again.

Chapter 21

CONCLUSION

We know those things are true
By believing, not by seeing.

2 Corinthians 5: 7

It is now December, 1998, roughly 10 months since my stem cell transplant. I see my personal oncologist regularly. I am continuing the aridea treatments. The basis for my recovery started with a fine medical team at Yale New Haven Oncology Department.

It has been 14 years since I was initially diagnosed with lymphoma. It is amazing to me to notice the difference in the way I approach life. I never put off what needs to be done today. I no longer count the days wondering if I am going to die.

I will live a beautiful life as long as God wants me to.

Every chance I get I go to Newport, RI, with my husband. Jim and I have a condominium right on the bay. This is where I often go. They say water is mysterious and also inspirational. I look at the beautiful life God has given me, and I thank Him for His goodness.

Hearing the waves roll to the shore is peaceful for me. All through my stem cell transplant, I dreamed of this moment. The sun is shining with a slight overcast, and the waves are beating softly in front of me. It has been a year since my stem cell transplant. Jim and I have been married 33 years. I've turned 53. The six-month CAT scan since the transplant showed no sign of cancer. I am cancer free. I have many reasons to celebrate!

Here we are in the church for my grandson's baptism. That's me, Tom, Jake, Tracey and Jim.

Jake

My daughter and her husband informed Jim and me that we were going to be grandparents.

Throughout my treatments the biggest prayer I said every night was "Let my daughter enjoy the beauty of having a child." I never wanted to leave this earth thinking she wouldn't become a mother. Tracey and Tom had so much trouble starting a family. Fertility drugs didn't work. I kept telling both of them that when I was finished with my stem cell procedure, their day would come. I never stopped praying. I always believed Tracey would get pregnant. My dream came true for her. We had so much fun picking out clothes, having a baby shower, and reading books on the stages of birth.

On September 13, 1998, Tracey and Tom had a beautiful baby boy. They named him Jake Thomas Bentz. I was fortunate to be at the hospital for the birth of my grandson.

When Tom called me to come into the room to see my

That's Tracey and my grandson Jake.

My daughter (with Jake sleeping) is in the center with some of her cousins: Michelle, Diane, Lori and Gina.

Four generations of my family are featured here (left to right): Tracey, Jake, Jim and great grandma Ida. This photo was taken on Easter Day, 1999.

grandson, it was like a feeling I could not explain. I was so happy to be alive to see my daughter give birth to her son. Jake had the biggest eyes I have ever seen. He had a lot of hair. He couldn't stop looking around the room. It was as if he were saying, "Here I am." This moment I will never forget. As each day goes by, I appreciate my sister's Patty and Susan words: "There is nothing like a grandchild".

I receive great pleasure to see Jake's smile and have a feeling of joy to see a new life. It is great to see the innocence of a child. We are all so lucky.

Soon it will be two years since I underwent treatment. I still show no sign of disease. Time is passing quickly. I am now back to work almost full time. I enjoy my job and the clients I see every day. I often talk about my transplant and share my ordeal to those who need to understand what I went through. I try to help anyone who calls me or enters the shop to tell me about his or her fears about cancer. I reassure them that I will be there for them.

64 My Detour

Just six months, Jake keeps me going these days.

It is interesting to know that stem cell transplants are now used to treat other diseases in addition to cancer. In just two years many advances have been made.

Life is what you make of it. I often wonder why we wait until a tragedy occurs before we start to live. I remember I was always a person who needed to save money for the future. But now I live. I try to be positive and I want to make the best out of every situation. I learned to take one day at a time.

I applaud the procedure for saving my life and the medical team who worked so hard in this field of stem cell transplant. Dr. Cooper and his staff will never be forgotten.

Writing this book wasn't easy. I relived each phase of the stem cell transplant. Emotionally it was a difficult form of therapy.

I recall at one of my group meetings, a man said that his transplant was easy, and he would do it again if needed. I feel the same way he does. I only hope I can help someone who has to go through this ordeal and make them understand you can do it!

I never thought I would see this day since I was diagnosed at the age of 39. Time heals everything. I no longer wake up thinking of only cancer in my life. I know someday I will die, but today I want to live. I want to learn something new. Maybe some day there will be another detour. If so, I will fight to live, for my family and friends... especially my husband... my daughter... and my grandchild.

Final Thought

We must fight to stay alive.
There is always a light at the end of the tunnel.
Never give up.
It is not how long we live that is important,
it is how well we live that is important.

We are on this earth for just a short time,
what we do on earth,
and what we say on earth
is what we leave behind.
For we shall not pass this way again.
Peace be with you.

That's me and I'm off to Disneyland to celebrate my health after many months of treatments and rehabilitation. Stem-cell transplant enabled me to have another chance at life.

BIBLIOGRAPHY

National Cancer Institute Publication *"What You Need To Know About Non-Hodg Lymphomas"*

"Consent For Participation in a Research Project, Yale University School of Medicine" University.

"The Way", Illustrated edition of *"The Living Bible,"* Tyndale House Publish Wheaton, Illinois.

A Survivor's Story

The road to recovery involves treatment, family support, doctrine, wading through insurance forms and controlling emotions, especially fear.

In 1985, **Rosemary Champagne** was diagnosed with lymphoma.

Her courageous story of recovery through faith and stem cell transplant will motivate others and assist a family and its friends when a loved one gallantly fights illness.

Born in New Britain and raised in Southington where she owns a hair salon, Champagne has overcome cancer. She credits stem cell transplant for giving her "a second chance" at life.